This workbook has been written and developed to be used alongside the Lonsdale revision guide, **AQA GCSE Biology Essentials**, to help you get the most out of your revision. You can use it if you are studying AQA GCSE Biology Foundation or Higher Tier.

It contains 'quick fire' questions, including multiple choice questions, matching pair exercises and short answer questions, to test your understanding of the topics covered in the revision guide.

Start by reading through a topic in the revision guide. Make notes, jotting down anything that you think will help you to remember the information. When you have finished, take a short break and then read through your notes. You might even want to try covering them up and writing them out again from memory.

Finally, work through the relevant questions in this workbook without looking at the guide or your notes.

The page headers and sub-headings in this workbook correspond with those in your revision guide, so that you can easily identify the questions that relate to each topic.

Completing the questions will help to reinforce your understanding of the topic covered in the guide and highlight any areas that need further revision.

The answers to the questions in this workbook are available in a separate booklet. There is a box at the end of each page for you to record your score. Don't worry if you get some questions wrong the first time. Just re-read the information in your revision guide and try again.

The tick boxes on the contents page let you track your revision progress: just put a tick in the box next to each topic when you're confident that you understand it.

Good luck with your exams!

**ISBN 978-1-905896-50-9**

Published by Lonsdale, a division of Huveaux Plc.

**Project Editor:** Katie Galloway
**Editors:** Ali March and Robert Dean
**Cover Design:** Angela English
**Concept Design:** Sarah Duxbury and Helen Jacobs
**Design:** Little Red Dog Design
Lonsdale
**Artwork:** Lonsdale and HL Studios

# Contents

# Contents

# The Nervous System

## The Parts of the Nervous System

**1** **a)** What does the central nervous system (CNS) consist of? Tick the correct option.

A  Brain and effectors ◯          B  Brain and spinal cord ◯

C  Spinal cord and receptors ◯    D  Receptors and effectors ◯

**b)** Which structure is a sensory receptor? Tick the correct option.

A  The liver ◯                    B  The kidney ◯

C  The skin ◯                     D  The stomach ◯

**c)** What is another name given to nerve cells? Tick the correct option.

A  Capillaries ◯                  B  Effectors ◯

C  Neurones ◯                     D  Receptors ◯

## The Three Types of Neurone

**2** Fill in the missing words to complete the following sentences.

The ............................... neurones receive messages from the receptors and send them to the CNS.

The ............................... neurones send messages from the CNS to the effectors.

These two neurones are connected in the CNS by a ............................... neurone.

**3** An electrical signal only travels in one direction down a neurone.

Is this statement **true** or **false**? ...............................

## Connections Between Neurones

**4** **a)** What is the name of the gap between two nerve cells?

.......................................................................................

**b)** What happens when an electrical, or nervous, impulse reaches the gap between two neurones?
Tick the correct option.

A  The impulse stops ◯

B  The impulse jumps the gap ◯

C  A chemical transmitter is released ◯

D  A hormone is released ◯

## Types of Receptor

**1** List three stimuli and the receptors used to detect them.

**a)** .............................................................................................

**b)** .............................................................................................

**c)** .............................................................................................

**2** **a)** Which of the following shows the correct sequence of events in the passage of a nerve impulse? Tick the correct option.

**A**  Effector → Receptor → Sensory neurone → CNS → Motor neurone  ◯

**B**  Receptor → Sensory neurone → CNS → Motor neurone → Effector  ◯

**C**  Receptor → Motor neurone → CNS → Sensory neurone → Effector  ◯

**D**  Effector → Sensory neurone → CNS → Motor neurone → Receptor  ◯

**b)** Which part of the nervous system acts as the coordinator in the passage of a nerve impulse? Tick the correct option.

**A**  Effector  ◯                          **B**  Receptor  ◯

**C**  Brain  ◯                             **D**  Central Nervous System (CNS)  ◯

## Reflex Action

**3** **a)** Fill in the missing words to complete the following sentences.

In a ................................... action the electrical impulse does not enter the conscious areas of

your brain. The time between the stimulus and the ................................... is as short as possible.

The only three neurones involved in a reflex action are the sensory neurones, the

................................... neurones and the ................................... neurones.

**b)** Sometimes conscious action is too slow to prevent harm to the body. A reflex action speeds up the response time by missing out the brain completely.

Which of the following is an example of a reflex action? Tick the correct option.

**A**  Looking both ways to cross the road  ◯          **B**  Removing your hand from a hot plate  ◯

**C**  Laughing at a joke  ◯                           **D**  Whistling to get someone's attention  ◯

◻

# Internal Environment and Hormones

## Internal Conditions

**1** **a)** Fill in the missing words to complete the following sentences.

Humans need to keep their internal _____ relatively _____.

This is done by _____ things such as temperature and water content.

**b)** The amount of water in the body must be controlled. Suggest three ways in which water is removed from the body.

**i)** _____

**ii)** _____

**iii)** _____

**c)** How does the body take in ions? Tick the correct option.

**A** By sweating ⬭    **B** By breathing ⬭

**C** By eating and drinking ⬭    **D** By excretion ⬭

**d)** How is glucose used up? Tick the correct option.

**A** As energy in movement ⬭    **B** In keeping cool ⬭

**C** In digestion ⬭    **D** In sweating ⬭

## Hormones

**2** **a)** Where are hormones produced?

_____

**b)** How are hormones transported around the body? Tick the correct option.

**A** By the nervous system ⬭    **B** In the air we breathe in ⬭

**C** By the skin ⬭    **D** In the bloodstream ⬭

**3** **a)** Which hormone is produced by the pituitary gland? Tick the correct option.

**A** Adrenalin ⬭    **B** FSH ⬭

**C** Oestrogen ⬭    **D** Progesterone ⬭

**b)** Which hormone is produced by the ovaries? Tick the correct option.

**A** Adrenalin ⬭    **B** FSH ⬭

**C** Oestrogen ⬭    **D** LH ⬭

# Internal Environment and Hormones

## Natural Control of Fertility

Revision Guide Reference: Page 14

**1 a)** The diagram represents the female reproductive system. Label the main parts.

A ...................................................

B ...................................................

**b)** Draw lines between the boxes to match each hormone to its function.

| Hormone | Function |
|---------|----------|
| FSH | Stimulates the release of an egg |
| Oestrogen | Causes the ovaries to produce oestrogen |
| LH | Slows down the production of FSH |

## Artificial Control of Fertility

**1 a)** Which of the following is a treatment for infertile couples? Tick the correct option.

A  Contraception ⬭    B  Ovulation ⬭

C  IVF ⬭    D  LH ⬭

**b)** Which of the following can be used as an oral contraceptive? Tick the correct option.

A  Progesterone ⬭    B  FSH ⬭

C  LH ⬭    D  Oestrogen ⬭

**c) i)** How is FSH used in the artificial control of fertility?

.................................................................................................................................................

.................................................................................................................................................

**ii)** How is oestrogen used in the artificial control of fertility?

.................................................................................................................................................

.................................................................................................................................................

.................................................................................................................................................

# Diet

## Metabolic Rate

**1** What does the term **metabolic rate** refer to? Tick the correct option.

    **A**   How quickly the heart beats ☐

    **B**   How quickly food is digested ☐

    **C**   How quickly chemical reactions in our body cells take place ☐

    **D**   How quickly we exercise ☐

**2** Circle the correct options in the following sentences.

Your metabolic rate stays **low / high** for some time after **exercise / sleep.** The more exercise you take, the fitter you are likely to be. The more exercise you take, the **more / less** food you need.

## Healthy Diets

**3 a)** A combination of what two things are needed to keep the body healthy?

    **i)** _____        **ii)** _____

**b)** Which of the following diseases might a person suffer from if they are overweight? Tick the **four** correct options.

    **A**  Arthritis ☐         **B**  Diabetes ☐

    **C**  Cystic fibrosis ☐         **D**  Anorexia nervosa ☐

    **E**  Low blood pressure ☐         **F**  Sickle cell anaemia ☐

    **G**  Heart disease ☐         **H**  Stroke ☐

**c)** What is the name given to diseases caused by a lack of vitamins and minerals? Tick the correct option.

    **A**  Inadequacy diseases ☐         **B**  Insufficiency diseases ☐

    **C**  Diet diseases ☐         **D**  Deficiency diseases ☐

**d)** What is the cause of malnourishment? Tick the correct option.

    **A**  Not enough vitamins in the diet ☐         **B**  Not eating enough food ☐

    **C**  Not eating a balanced diet ☐         **D**  Not enough protein in the diet ☐

**e)** Are you more likely to be obese if you live in the **developed** world or the **developing** world?

_____

**f)** Are you more likely to have problems due to the lack of food in the **developed** world or the

**developing** world? _____ ☐

        © Lonsdale

## Cholesterol

**1 a)** Where is cholesterol made in the body? Tick the correct option.

**A** The heart ⬭  **B** The liver ⬭

**C** The kidneys ⬭  **D** The stomach ⬭

**b)** Circle the correct options in the following sentences.

Cholesterol is found in the **blood / kidneys**. The level of cholesterol is influenced by **diet / exercise** and inherited factors. Cholesterol is carried in the blood by **hormones / lipoproteins**.

**2 a)** What does LDL stand for?

_____

**b)** What does HDL stand for?

_____

**c)** Which of the following is classed as 'bad' cholesterol? Tick the correct option.

**A** HDL ⬭  **B** LDL ⬭

**C** GDL ⬭  **D** BDL ⬭

## Fats and Salts

**3** Which of the following types of fats increases blood cholesterol and blood sugar levels? Tick the correct option.

**A** Saturated fats ⬭  **B** Monounsaturated fats ⬭

**C** Polyunsaturated fats ⬭  **D** Vegetable oil ⬭

**4** What can happen if a person's diet contains too much salt? Tick the correct option.

**A** Blood pressure goes down ⬭  **B** Cholesterol is reduced ⬭

**C** Blood pressure goes up ⬭  **D** Mineral ion levels are reduced ⬭

**5** Why is it better to prepare your own meals from raw ingredients than to buy processed food and ready meals?

_____

_____

# Drugs

## Drugs

**1** Which two sources can drugs be made from?

a) _____

b) _____

## Developing New Drugs

**2 a)** Fill in the missing words to complete the sentences below.

New medical drugs must be _____ and _____ to find out

whether they are _____.

They must then be checked for _____.

**b)** What does **toxic** mean?

_____

_____

## Thalidomide

**3 a)** Which condition was thalidomide first developed to treat? Tick the correct option.

A Insomnia ⬭          B Depression ⬭

C Obesity ⬭          D Heart disease ⬭

**b)** Why did pregnant women start to take thalidomide? Tick the correct option.

A It prevented miscarriage ⬭          B It stopped morning sickness ⬭

C It stopped multiple births ⬭          D It prevented ovulation ⬭

**c)** What were the effects of taking thalidomide during pregnancy? Tick the correct option.

A Women gave birth prematurely ⬭

B Babies were born with severe limb abnormalities ⬭

C Women had multiple births ⬭

D Babies had a high birth weight ⬭

**d)** Which disease is thalidomide now used to treat?

_____

_____

## Legal and Illegal Drugs

**1** Fill in the missing words to complete the sentences below.

Illegal drugs, such as heroin and ........................................., and legal drugs, such as

......................................... and tobacco are used by some people for ......................................... . But they

can be very ......................................... .

Drugs alter chemical processes in the body so people can become ......................................... to them.

**2** Which of the following drugs are legal? Tick the **three** correct options.

**A** Heroin ◯      **B** Ecstasy ◯

**C** Alcohol ◯      **D** Cannabis ◯

**E** Nicotine ◯      **F** Caffeine ◯

## Alcohol and Tobacco

**3** **a)** What is the addictive substance found in tobacco? Tick the correct option.

**A** Tar ◯      **B** Cannabis ◯

**C** Ash ◯      **D** Nicotine ◯

**b)** Which gas, found in cigarette smoke, prevents red blood cells from carrying oxygen?
Tick the correct option.

**A** Oxygen ◯      **B** Carbon dioxide ◯

**C** Carbon monoxide ◯      **D** Nitrogen ◯

**c)** Smoking during pregnancy can deprive the developing fetus of oxygen. How might this affect the birth mass of the baby?

.......................................................................................................................................................................

**d)** Smoking can cause a number of harmful diseases. Name two diseases caused by smoking cigarettes.

**i)** ............................................................      **ii)** ............................................................

**4** **a)** Which two organs are affected by drinking too much alcohol? Tick the correct option.

**A** Heart and stomach ◯      **B** Brain and liver ◯

**C** Kidneys and liver ◯      **D** Brain and heart ◯

**b)** Why are car accidents more likely to happen if the driver is under the influence of alcohol?

◯

.......................................................................................................................................................................

# Pathogens

**1** What are pathogens?

_____

**2** (Circle) the correct words in the following sentences.

Viruses are **smaller / bigger** than bacteria. They reproduce **slowly / quickly** inside living cells. They produce **toxins / antitoxins**, and cause illnesses.

**3 a)** Which of the following is a disease caused by a bacterium? Tick the correct option.

**A** Ringworm ◯      **B** Food poisoning ◯

**C** Polio ◯      **D** Tuberculosis ◯

**E** Measles ◯      **F** Cancer ◯

**b)** Which of the following is a disease caused by a virus? Tick the correct option.

**A** Tetanus ◯      **B** Flu ◯

**C** Athlete's foot ◯      **D** Ringworm ◯

**E** Cholera ◯      **F** Cancer ◯

**4** Which part of our blood defends the body against infection? Tick the correct option.

**A** Red blood cells ◯      **B** Plasma ◯

**C** Platelets ◯      **D** White blood cells ◯

**5 a)** What do antitoxins do? Tick the **two** correct options.

**A** They destroy the toxins produced by viruses ◯

**B** They destroy the antibodies produced by bacteria ◯

**C** They destroy the toxins produced by bacteria ◯

**D** They destroy the antigens produced by viruses ◯

**b)** What do antibodies do? Tick the correct option.

**A** They destroy the toxins produced by pathogens ◯

**B** They attack healthy body cells ◯

**C** They destroy certain pathogens ◯

**D** They ingest pathogens ◯

## Treatment of Disease

**1** Which of the following is an example of a painkiller? Tick the correct option.

**A** Alcohol ◯      **B** Aspirin ◯

**C** Insulin ◯      **D** Vitamin ◯

**2** Fill in the missing words to complete the sentences below.

The symptoms of a disease can often be alleviated using _____. However, these drugs

do not _____ pathogens. Antibiotics can be used to kill infective

_____ pathogens. But they cannot kill _____ pathogens, which

live and _____ inside the body's cells.

**3 a)** Give an example of a strain of bacteria which has developed resistance to antibiotics.

_____

**b)** By what process do bacteria develop resistance to antibiotics?

_____

## Vaccination

**4 a)** What do vaccines contain? Tick the correct option.

**A** Medical drugs ◯      **B** Antibiotics ◯

**C** Dead / harmless forms of the disease ◯      **D** Antibodies ◯

**b)** Write **true** or **false** alongside each of the following statements about vaccines.

**i)** Red blood cells produce antibodies. _____

**ii)** Antibiotics destroy the antibodies. _____

**iii)** A live pathogen is injected into your body. _____

**iv)** Vaccines provide an acquired immunity. _____

**c)** Which three illnesses does the MMR vaccine protect against?

**i)** _____    **ii)** _____

**iii)** _____

◯

# Competition and Adaptations

## Population and Communities

**1** Which of the following statements is the correct definition of the word **population**? Tick the correct option.

A   The total number of organisms living in a particular habitat

B   The total number of individuals of the same species living in a particular habitat

C   The total number of animals living in a particular habitat

D   The total number of plants living in a particular habitat

**2** Which of the following statements describes a **community**? Tick the correct option.

A   A group of animals and plants interacting with one another

B   A population of animals

C   Animals adapted to their surroundings

D   A food chain

## Competition

**3** Which of the following do animals need to compete for? Tick the **three** correct options.

A   Light              B   Food

C   Water              D   Space

**4** What do plants compete for that animals do not? Tick the correct option.

A   Light              B   Nutrients

C   Space              D   Water

**5 a)** Fill in the missing words to complete the sentence.

When organisms compete, those which are ................................ ................................ to

their environment are more ................................ and usually exist in ................................

numbers.

**b)** What would you expect to happen to the population size of an organism that was less well adapted to its environment than another?

................................................................................................................................

................................................................................................................................

# Competition and Adaptations

## Adaptations

**1 a)** Which of the following statements best describes what the word **adaptation** means? Tick the correct option.

**A** A significant change in the size of a population

**B** A feature that develops to make an organism better suited to its environment

**C** The process by which the different organisms in a habitat learn to share resources

**D** A characteristic that is acquired by an individual, e.g. a scar

**b)** What is the advantage of an adaptation?

**2 a)** Briefly describe the conditions in which a polar bear lives.

**b)** Which of the following are adaptations of the polar bear? Tick the correct option(s).

**A** Large ears

**B** Thick coat

**C** Layer of fat under skin

**D** Small feet

**E** Camouflage

**F** Large surface area to volume ratio

**3** Cacti have spines instead of leaves. How do these spines help them to survive? Tick the **two** correct options.

**A** They help to trap and store rain water

**B** They reflect the Sun's heat

**C** They minimise surface area to reduce water loss

**D** They make the plant look like a predator

**E** They prevent animals from eating the plant

**F** They trap insects, which the plant feeds on

# Genetics

## Genetic Information

**1** What are the sections of chromosome called that control our characteristics? Tick the correct option.

    **A** Genes ◯         **B** DNA ◯

    **C** Helix ◯         **D** Amino acids ◯

**2** How many pairs of chromosomes do humans have?

_____

## Variation

**3** Which of the following characteristics are due to genetic variation? Tick the correct options.

    **A** Eye colour ◯         **B** Religion ◯

    **C** Tongue rolling ability ◯         **D** Weight ◯

**4** Which of the following characteristics are due to environmental variation? Tick the correct options.

    **A** Accent ◯         **B** Eye colour ◯

    **C** Weight ◯         **D** Scars ◯

## Reproduction and Variation

**5** Which type of reproduction involves only one parent? Tick the correct option.

    **A** Asexual reproduction ◯         **B** Sexual reproduction ◯

    **C** Evolution ◯         **D** Natural selection ◯

**6 a)** Which type of reproduction leads to variation? Tick the correct option.

    **A** Evolution ◯         **B** Sexual reproduction ◯

    **C** Natural selection ◯         **D** Asexual reproduction ◯

  **b)** Briefly explain why there is variation in the offspring of this type of reproduction.

_____

_____

**7** What are clones? Tick the correct option.

    **A** Genetically identical individuals ◯         **B** Genetically different individuals ◯

    **C** Individuals formed by sexual reproduction ◯         **D** Individuals that show variation ◯

## Reproducing Plants

**1** By which method do plants reproduce naturally? Tick the correct option.

**A** Sexually ◯      **B** Genetic modification ◯

**C** Asexually ◯      **D** Embryo transplantation ◯

**2** Which of the following statements about the offspring of asexual reproduction are true? Tick the **two** correct options.

**A** They show genetic variation ◯

**B** They are infertile ◯

**C** They are genetically identical to each other ◯

**D** They are genetically identical to the parent plant ◯

**E** They have stunted growth ◯

**F** They are prone to disease ◯

## Cloning Techniques

**3 a)** Which of the following techniques is suitable for cloning plants? Tick the **two** correct options.

**A** Taking cuttings ◯      **B** Embryo transplantation ◯

**C** Fusion cell ◯      **D** Tissue culture ◯

**E** Computer-aided synthesis ◯

**b)** Which of the following techniques is suitable for cloning animals? Tick the **two** correct options.

**A** Taking cuttings ◯      **B** Embryo transplantation ◯

**C** Fusion cell ◯      **D** Tissue culture ◯

**E** Computer-aided synthesis ◯

**4** Are the following statements **true** or **false**? Write your answers in the spaces provided.

**a)** A tissue culture technique produces offspring that are genetically identical to the parent plant.

**b)** Embryo transplantation produces offspring that are identical to the parents.

**c)** In adult cell cloning, the DNA from a donor animal is inserted into an empty egg cell.

**d)** Adult cell cloning produces offspring that are genetically identical to the parent animal.

# Genetics

## Genetic Modification

**1** (Circle) the correct options in the following sentences.

Genetic modification is a process in which genetic information from one **cell / organism** is transferred into another.

The genes are often transferred at a(n) **early / late** stage of development, so that the organism will develop with the desired **behaviour / characteristics**.

More organisms with the same characteristics can be produced if the genetically modified organism is then **cloned / reproduced**.

**2** Give three reasons why genetic modification may be used in the production of food crops.

a) ................................................................ b) ................................................................

c) ................................................................

## Insulin Production

**3** Which organism is used to produce genetically modified insulin? Tick the correct option.

**A** Bacteria ◯ **B** Fungi ◯

**C** Insects ◯ **D** Viruses ◯

**4** Which disease is the hormone insulin used to treat? Tick the correct option.

**A** Diabetes ◯ **B** Cystic fibrosis ◯

**C** High blood pressure ◯ **D** Anaemia ◯

## The Great Genetics Debate

**5** Genetic engineering is a process that involves changing the genetic material of an organism. List three advantages of genetic engineering.

a) ................................................................

b) ................................................................

c) ................................................................

**6** Scientists have made great advances in their understanding of genes. However, some people are concerned that this knowledge may be misused. Suggest two ways in which this knowledge could potentially be misused.

a) ................................................................

b) ................................................................

## The Theory of Evolution

**1** When did life forms first exist on Earth? Tick the correct option.

A  300 years ago ◯           B  3 million years ago ◯

C  3 billion years ago ◯     D  We don't know ◯

**2** What provides evidence for evolution? Tick the correct option.

A  Animals ◯                 B  Fossils ◯

C  Plants ◯                  D  Viruses ◯

## Evolution by Natural Selection

**3** Fill in the missing words to complete the following sentences.

Evolution is the change in a _____ over many generations. It may result in the formation

of a new _____, the members of which are better _____ to their environment.

**4** What is another name for evolution by natural selection? Tick the correct option.

A  Creationism ◯            B  Survival of the fittest ◯

C  Genetic modification ◯   D  Asexual reproduction ◯

**5 a)** If a dark coloured moth appears in a population of light coloured moths, what has happened?
Tick the correct option.

A  A miracle has occurred ◯         B  A genetic modification has occurred ◯

C  A mistake has occurred ◯         D  A mutation has occurred ◯

**b)** Under what circumstances might there be a change in the population of moths, where the number of dark coloured moths becomes greater than the number of light coloured moths?
Tick the correct option.

A  The dark moths eat the light coloured moths ◯

B  The dark moths are better adapted to the environment ◯

C  The male moths find the dark females more attractive ◯

D  The dark colouring is caused by an infectious disease ◯

## Extinction of Species

**6** Give three factors that could contribute to the extinction of a species.

a) _____      b) _____      c) _____      ◯

# Pollution

## The Population Explosion

**1** Which of the following effects have been created by an increase in the human population? Tick the **two** correct options.

**A** Less land available for plants and animals ◯

**B** Less waste being produced ◯

**C** A reduction in pollution ◯

**D** An increase in non-renewable energy sources being used ◯

**2** The human population is increasing exponentially. What does **exponentially** mean?

## Pollution

**3** Which of the following gases pollute the air? Tick the **three** correct options.

**A** Oxygen ◯      **B** Carbon dioxide ◯

**C** Methane ◯      **D** Nitrogen ◯

**E** Sulfur dioxide ◯      **F** Chlorine ◯

**4** Which of the following are ways that smoke and waste gases from a power station can damage the environment? Tick the **three** correct options.

**A** Cause acid rain ◯      **B** Decrease global warming ◯

**C** Kill trees and plants ◯      **D** Increase carbon dioxide ◯

**5 a)** Name two pollutants that can affect the land.

i) ..............................................................................................................................

ii) ..............................................................................................................................

**b)** Name two pollutants that can affect the water in our rivers and lakes.

i) ..............................................................................................................................

ii) ..............................................................................................................................

## Indicators of Pollution

**6** Give one example of a living organism that can be used as an indicator of pollution.

..............................................................................................................................

◯

## Deforestation

**1** What is deforestation? Tick the correct option.

    **A** Planting new trees ◯

    **B** Forest fires caused by hot weather ◯

    **C** Cutting down large areas of forest ◯

    **D** Polluting national parks with litter ◯

**2** Give two reasons for large-scale deforestation.

    **a)** ...............................................................................................................................................

    **b)** ...............................................................................................................................................

**3** What is the name of the gas given off when trees are burned? Tick the correct option.

    **A** Carbon dioxide ◯

    **B** Oxygen ◯

    **C** Methane ◯

    **D** Hydrogen ◯

**4** Which biological process decreases the amount of carbon dioxide in the atmosphere?
Tick the correct option.

    **A** Respiration ◯     **B** Exhalation ◯

    **C** Photosynthesis ◯     **D** Deforestation ◯

**5** **a)** Circle the correct options in the sentences below.

When deforestation occurs in **tropical / arctic / desert** regions, it has a devastating impact on the environment.

The loss of **trees / animals / insects** means less photosynthesis takes place, so less **oxygen / nitrogen / carbon dioxide** is removed from the atmosphere.

It also leads to a reduction in **variation / biodiversity / mutation**, because some tree species may become **devolved / damaged / extinct** and **habitats / land / farms** are being destroyed.

    **b)** What does **biodiversity** mean?

...............................................................................................................................................

# The Greenhouse Effect

## The Greenhouse Effect

**1** Fill in the missing words to complete the following sentences.

Some ........................................ in the atmosphere prevent ........................................ from escaping

into space. This is called the greenhouse effect.

The greenhouse effect is leading to global ........................................ .

**2** Name two gases that contribute to the greenhouse effect.

**a)** ........................................................................................................................................................................

**b)** ........................................................................................................................................................................

**3** Which of the following factors contribute to an increase in greenhouse gases?
Tick the **four** correct options.

**A** Carbon offsetting ◯

**B** Deforestation ◯

**C** Burning fossil fuels ◯

**D** Using renewable energy sources ◯

**E** A growth in cattle farming ◯

**F** Growing rice ◯

**G** Forest management ◯

**4** Which of the following are the negative effects of global warming? Tick the **two** correct options.

**A** Climate change ◯

**B** Erosion of buildings ◯

**C** Deforestation ◯

**D** A rise in sea levels ◯

**E** An increase in available land ◯

**F** Warmer summers ◯

**5** Some people think that global warming does not affect them. Do you agree with them?
Explain your answer.

........................................................................................................................................................................

........................................................................................................................................................................

◯

## Sustainable Development

**1** Fill in the missing words to complete the following sentences.

Sustainable development ensures that development can take place to help **improve / reduce / compromise** or sustain quality of life, without compromising the needs of future **space travel / generations / mutations**. It is an important consideration at local, regional and **sea / carbon dioxide / global** levels.

**2** List the three key areas that sustainable development is concerned with.

a) ........................................................................................................

b) ........................................................................................................

c) ........................................................................................................

**3** Briefly explain what sustainable resources are.

........................................................................................................

........................................................................................................

**4** **a)** How can we maintain ocean fish stocks? Tick the correct option.

**A** Increase fishing ⬜          **B** Increase fish farms ⬜

**C** Introduce quotas ⬜          **D** Stop eating fish ⬜

**b)** Give one other method used to help maintain ocean fish stocks.

........................................................................................................

**5** **a)** How can we maintain our forests and woodland? Tick the correct option.

**A** Have fewer national parks ⬜

**B** Build more houses ⬜

**C** Restock forests ⬜

**D** Increase the burning of fossil fuels ⬜

**b)** What is the key principle behind sustainable forest management?

........................................................................................................

**c)** Give two reasons why it is important to maintain our forests and woodland.

i) ........................................................................................................

ii) ........................................................................................................

⬜

# Cells

## Cells

**1** **a)** Circle the correct options in the following sentences.

    **i)** **Muscles / organs / cells / tissues** are the building blocks of life.

    **ii)** All **living / material / non-living / plastic** things are made up of cells.

    **iii)** A living thing is called a(n) **organelle / organism / human / mitochondria**.

**b)** Fill in the missing words to complete the following sentence.

The chemical reactions in a cell are controlled by ............................................................ . These are found in

............................................................ and ............................................................ .

## Animal Cells

**2** Look at this diagram of an animal cell.

**a)** What is the name of part A?
Tick the correct option.

    **A** Nucleus ⬭

    **B** Cell wall ⬭

    **C** Cell membrane ⬭

    **D** Cytoplasm ⬭

**b)** What is the name of part B? Tick the correct option.

    **A** Nucleus ⬭          **B** Cell wall ⬭

    **C** Cell membrane ⬭       **D** Cytoplasm ⬭

**c)** What is the name of part C? Tick the correct option.

    **A** Nucleus ⬭          **B** Cell wall ⬭

    **C** Cell membrane ⬭       **D** Cytoplasm ⬭

## Plant Cells

**3** Give three differences between an animal cell and a plant cell.

**a)** ............................................................................................................................................

**b)** ............................................................................................................................................

**c)** ............................................................................................................................................

# Diffusion and Osmosis

## The Movement of Substances

1  Cells have to replace substances that are used up, and remove waste products. They do this by osmosis and diffusion. Choose the correct word(s) from the options given to complete the following sentence.

**glucose**　　　　　**carbon dioxide**　　　　　**carbon monoxide**　　　　　**oxygen**

One of the waste products that will diffuse out of a cell is ............................................................................ .

## Diffusion

2  **a)**　Where does diffusion take place? Tick the correct option.

**A**　In solids and liquids　　　◯

**B**　In gases only　　　◯

**C**　In solutions and solids　　　◯

**D**　In gases and solutions　　　◯

**b)**　When does diffusion take place? Tick the correct option.

**A**　When there is no concentration gradient　　　◯

**B**　When there is a net movement of particles　　　◯

**C**　When there is movement from a low to a high concentration　　　◯

**D**　When there is melting of a solid　　　◯

## Osmosis

3  What is 'osmosis'?

.......................................................................................................................................................................

.......................................................................................................................................................................

4  What does 'partially permeable' mean? Tick the correct option.

**A**　Allows all substances to pass through　　　◯

**B**　Allows no substances to pass through　　　◯

**C**　Allows substances to pass through in one direction only　　　◯

**D**　Allows some substances to pass through　　　◯

# Photosynthesis

## Plant Mineral Requirements

**1** Fill in the missing words to complete the following sentence.

Plants need mineral _____ , which they absorb from the _____

through their _____ .

**2** Why does a plant need nitrates? Tick the correct option.

    **A**  To make DNA and cell membranes

    **B**  To make enzymes

    **C**  To form proteins

    **D**  To make chlorophyll

**3** Choose the correct words from the options given to complete the following sentence.

**make DNA and cell membranes**                      **make enzymes**

**form proteins and DNA**                             **make cholorophyll**

A plant needs magnesium to _____ .

## Photosynthesis

**4** Which of the following is the equation for photosynthesis? Tick the correct option.

    **A**  Glucose + Carbon dioxide ⟶ Oxygen + Water

    **B**  Glucose + Oxygen ⟶ Carbon monoxide + Water

    **C**  Glucose + Water ⟶ Carbon dioxide + Oxygen

    **D**  Carbon dioxide + Water ⟶ Glucose + Oxygen

**5** **a)**  Apart from carbon dioxide and water, what two other factors are required for photosynthesis?

      **i)** _____

      **ii)** _____

  **b)**  **i)**  What is the name of the pigment that absorbs the Sun's energy during photosynthesis?

      _____

      **ii)**  Where is this pigment found?

      _____

# Factors Affecting Photosynthesis

## Factors Affecting Photosynthesis

1. Which of the following are factors that can limit the rate of photosynthesis? Tick the **three** correct options.

   A   Amount of oxygen ◯

   B   Amount of light ◯

   C   Amount of carbon dioxide ◯

   D   Amount of chlorophyll ◯

   E   Temperature ◯

## Temperature

2. Circle the correct option in the following sentence.

   The temperature at which enzymes controlling photosynthesis are destroyed is **25°C / 75°C / 14°C / 45°C**.

## Carbon Dioxide Concentration

3. A plant is receiving plenty of light but its rate of photosynthesis stops increasing. What other factors might be responsible? Tick the correct option.

   A   Amount of carbon dioxide or the amount of oxygen ◯

   B   Amount of carbon dioxide or the temperature ◯

   C   Amount of chlorophyll or the temperature ◯

   D   Amount of glucose or the amount of oxygen ◯

## Light Intensity

4. Explain why too little light can have a negative effect on a plant.

   _____

   _____

## Artificial Controls

5. Fill in the missing words to complete the following sentence.

   To control the rate of photosynthesis, _____ can be used to make plants grow

   more _____ , becoming bigger and _____ .

# Food Chains and Biomass

## Food Chains

**1** The text below represents a food chain.

**Rosebush** ➡ **Aphid** ➡ **Ladybird** ➡ **Blackbird**

Circle the correct options in the following sentences.

a) The producer in the food chain is the **aphid / blackbird / ladybird / rosebush**.

b) The herbivore in the food chain is the **aphid / blackbird / ladybird / rosebush**.

c) The top carnivore in the food chain is the **aphid / blackbird / ladybird / rosebush**.

**2** Where does the initial source of energy for all food chains come from? Tick the correct option.

A The Moon ⬭

B The Sun ⬭

C The soil ⬭

D Animals ⬭

**3** Briefly explain what biomass is.

_____

_____

## Pyramid of Biomass

**4** Energy is lost at all the stages in a food chain. What is the energy used for? Tick the **three** correct options.

A Photosynthesis ⬭

B Keeping warm ⬭

C Movement ⬭

D Growth ⬭

**5** Give three ways in which the efficiency of a food chain can be improved.

a) _____

b) _____

c) _____

## Recycling the Materials of Life

**1** Fill in the missing words to complete the following sentences.

Organisms _____ material from the environment for _____

and other purposes. These materials are _____ to the environment when the

organisms _____ .

**2** Give three factors that increase the rate at which microorganisms can digest materials.

**a)** _____ **b)** _____ **c)** _____

## The Carbon Cycle

**3** Using the diagram of the carbon cycle below, circle the correct options in the following sentences.

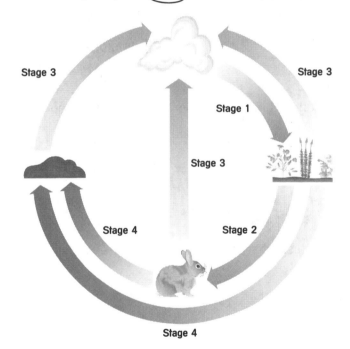

Stage 3   Stage 3

Stage 1

Stage 3

Stage 4   Stage 2

Stage 4

**a)** Stage 1 shows when **respiration / decomposition / photosynthesis / combustion** happens.

**b)** Stage 3 shows when **respiration / decomposition / photosynthesis / combustion** happens.

**c)** Stage 4 shows when **respiration / decomposition / photosynthesis / combustion** happens.

**4** At stage 2, carbon is converted into certain substances in the animal. What are these substances? Tick the correct option.

**A** Vitamins and minerals ◯   **B** Carbohydrates and proteins ◯

**C** Fats and fibre ◯   **D** Carbohydrates, fats and proteins ◯

# Enzymes

## Enzymes

**1** Circle the correct options in the following sentences.

**a)** An enzyme is a **biological / chemical** catalyst that **speeds up / slows down** the rate of **biological / chemical** reactions in an organism.

**b)** Enzymes are made from **carbohydrate / fat / vitamin / protein** molecules. They are made up of long chains of **DNA / amino acids / fatty acids / starch molecules**.

**2** Briefly explain what happens to an enzyme if the temperature goes too high.

_____

_____

## Aerobic Respiration

**3 a)** What gas is used in aerobic respiration? Tick the correct option.

**A** Carbon dioxide ◯          **B** Hydrogen ◯

**C** Oxygen ◯          **D** Nitrogen ◯

**b)** What gas is produced during aerobic respiration? Tick the correct option.

**A** Carbon dioxide ◻          **B** Hydrogen ◻

**C** Oxygen ◻          **D** Nitrogen ◻

## Enzymes Inside Living Cells

**4** Give three processes in living cells that can be speeded up by enzymes.

**a)** _____

**b)** _____

**c)** _____

**5** Choose the correct words from the options given to complete the following sentence.

**amino acids**          **muscles**          **molecules**          **proteins**          **temperature**

The energy released during respiration is used to build larger _____, enable

_____ to contract, maintain a constant _____ (in mammals

and birds) and to make _____ in plants from _____.

## Enzymes Outside Living Cells

Revision Guide Reference: Page 43

**1** Specialised cells in glands in the digestive system produce digestive enzymes.

**a)** What type of enzyme breaks down fat? Tick the correct option.

A  Protease  ☐

B  Carbohydrase  ☐

C  Cellulase  ☐

D  Lipase  ☐

**b)** What type of enzyme breaks down protein? Tick the correct option.

A  Protease  ☐

B  Carbohydrase  ☐

C  Cellulase  ☐

D  Lipase  ☐

**2** Which of the following organs produce digestive enzymes? Tick the **four** correct options.

A  Rectum  ☐

B  Large intestine  ☐

C  Salivary glands  ☐

D  Stomach  ☐

E  Gall bladder  ☐

F  Pancreas  ☐

G  Small intestine  ☐

H  Liver  ☐

**3 a)** What soluble product is produced by protease?

_____

**b)** What soluble product is produced by amylase?

_____

**c)** What two products are produced by lipase?

i) _____  ii) _____  ☐

# Enzymes

## Bile

**1 a)** Which organ produces bile? _____

**b)** Where is bile stored? _____

**c)** Into what part of the body is bile released? _____

**2** What are the jobs of bile? Tick the **two** correct options.

**A** To break down sugars ◯

**B** To neutralise stomach acid ◯

**C** To remove excess water ◯

**D** To break down protein ◯

**E** To emulsify fats ◯

**F** To break down carbohydrates ◯

## Use of Enzymes

**3** Which two enzymes might biological detergents contain? Tick the **two** correct options.

**A** Fat-digesting ◯

**B** Glucose-digesting ◯

**C** Bile-digesting ◯

**D** Protein-digesting ◯

**4** Match statements **A**, **B**, **C** and **D** with the enzymes **1–4** listed below. Write the appropriate numbers in the boxes provided.

**1** Lipases     **2** Carbohydrases

**3** Proteases    **4** Isomerases

**A** Digest fat stains from clothes ◯

**B** Used to produce fructose syrup used in slimming foods ◯

**C** Pre-digest protein in baby foods ◯

**D** Used to make chocolate and syrup ◯

# Controlling Body Conditions

## Controlling Body Conditions

**1** To function properly, what four things must the body control levels of?

a) ...........................................................................................................................

b) ...........................................................................................................................

c) ...........................................................................................................................

d) ...........................................................................................................................

## Blood Glucose Concentration

**2** What hormone is produced by the pancreas? Tick the correct option.

**A** ADH ◯

**B** Insulin ◯

**C** Glucose ◯

**D** Glycogen ◯

**3 a)** Apart from the pancreas, which other organ is involved in controlling blood sugar levels? Tick the correct option.

**A** Kidney ◯      **B** Liver ◯

**C** Brain ◯      **D** Heart ◯

**b)** What causes diabetes? Tick the correct option.

**A** Pancreas does not produce insulin ◯

**B** Liver does not produce glycogen ◯

**C** Kidneys do not remove glucose from the blood ◯

**D** Liver does not produce insulin ◯

## Water and Ion Content

**4** The body gains water and ions through food and drink. Fill in the missing words to complete the following sentences.

When the ........................................ or ........................................ content of the body is out of balance,

too much water may move in or out of the cells. This process is called ........................................ . ◯

# Body Temperature

## Body Temperature

**1 a)** Where are the receptors located that provide information about blood temperature? Tick the correct option.

**A** Skin ◯       **B** Brain ◯

**C** Kidneys ◯       **D** Lungs ◯

**b)** Circle the correct option in the following sentence.

The normal body temperature is **20°C / 100°C / 37°C / 75°C**.

**HT**

**2 a)** What changes occur if the body becomes too cold? Tick the **three** correct options.

**A** Blood vessels in the skin dilate ◯

**B** Sweat glands stop producing sweat ◯

**C** Shivering occurs ◯

**D** Skin becomes flushed ◯

**E** Blood vessels in the skin constrict ◯

**F** Heat loss increases ◯

**b)** Give two changes that occur if the body becomes too hot.

**i)** _____

**ii)** _____

## Removing Waste Products

**3** Choose the correct word from the options given to complete the following sentence.

**amino acids**      **glucose**      **urea**      **water**

The waste product removed by the kidneys is _____ .

**4** Which of the following are waste products that need to be removed from the body in order to maintain a constant internal environment? Tick the **two** correct options.

**A** Oxygen ◯       **B** Carbon dioxide ◯

**C** Blood ◯       **D** Urea ◯

# Chromosomes and Gametes

## Human Body Cells

**1** (Circle) the correct option in the following sentence.

Human body cells contain a total of **23 / 46 / 22 / 28** chromosomes.

**2** **a)** What are sex cells known as? Tick the correct option.

**A** Genes ◯                        **B** Alleles ◯

**C** Gametes ◯                      **D** Chromosomes ◯

**b)** What do sex cells contain? Tick the correct option.

**A** Half the number of chromosomes as a normal body cell ◯

**B** The same number of chromosomes as a normal body cell ◯

**C** Twice the number of chromosomes as a normal body cell ◯

**D** Half the number of chromosomes of a sperm cell ◯

**c)** What is produced from the fusion of two sex cells?

........................................................................................................................................................

## Inheritance of the Sex Chromosome

**3** **a)** Choose the correct chromosomes from the options given to complete the following sentence.

**XY and YY     XX and XY     XX and YY     XF and XM**

The sex chromosomes are ................................................... .

**b)** Which of the following are the female sex chromosomes, and which are the male sex chromosomes? Label them correctly.

**i)** ................................................

**ii)** ................................................

**4** What determines the sex of an individual?

........................................................................................................................................................

........................................................................................................................................................

# Cell Division

## Mitosis

**1** Mitosis is the division of body cells to make new cells.

**a)** When is mitosis not used in dividing cells? Tick the correct option.

**A** Asexual reproduction ◯    **B** Gamete production ◯

**C** Repair ◯    **D** Growth ◯

**b)** Fill in the missing words to complete the following sentences.

A copy of each _____ is made before a cell divides. The new cell has the same

_____ information as the _____ cell.

**c)** Circle the correct option in the following sentence.

When one cell has undergone mitosis, **1 / 2 / 4 / 8** 'daughter' cells will be made.

## HT Meiosis

**2 a)** Choose the correct words from the options given to complete the following sentence.

**ovaries        chromosomes        eggs**

Meiosis takes place in the _____ and testes, and produces _____

and sperm containing 23 _____ .

**b)** What is the name of the four types of cell produced after meiosis?

_____

## Fertilisation

**3** During fertilisation the male and female sex cells join.

**a)** What does the new body cell contain?

_____

**b)** What happens to the new body cell next?

_____ ◯

## Alleles

Revision Guide Reference: Page 49

**1** How many alleles does the gene controlling tongue-rolling ability have? Tick the correct option.

**A** One ◯

**B** Three ◯

**C** Four ◯

**D** Two ◯

**2** Fill in the missing words to complete the following sentences.

**a)** Where there are different alleles for a gene, one is known as the _____ gene

and the other is known as the _____ gene.

**b)** Using the correct genetic terms, describe the following alleles.

**i)** BB _____

**ii)** Bb _____

**iii)** bb _____

**3** Match definitions **A**, **B**, **C** and **D** with the keywords **1–4** listed below. Write the appropriate numbers in the boxes provided.

**1** Dominant                    **2** Phenotype

**3** Heterozygous                **4** Homozygous

    **A** What the organism looks like ◯

    **B** The stronger allele ◯

    **C** Both alleles are the same ◯

    **D** Different alleles ◯

**4** Fill in the missing words to complete the following sentences.

**a)** A _____ allele will control the characteristics of the gene if it's present on only one chromosome, or if it's present on both chromosomes.

**b)** A _____ allele will only control the characteristics of the gene if it's present on both chromosomes.

◻

# Genetic Diagrams

## Monohybrid Inheritance

**1 a)** When is it useful to draw a genetic cross diagram?

_____

**b)** What does a genetic cross diagram show?

_____

## Inheritance of Eye Colour

**2 a)** John has blue eyes. Both his parents have brown eyes. His mother's genotype is Bb. What must John's father's genotype be? Tick the correct option.

**A** Bb ◯          **B** BB ◯          **C** bb ◯          **D** BBb ◯

**b)** Circle the correct option in the following sentence.

If both parents have blue eyes there is a **50% / 100% / 0% / 24%** chance that they will have a child with brown eyes.

HT

**3 a)** Complete this genetic diagram to show the possible genotypes of the offspring.

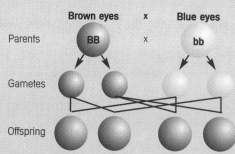

**b)** Complete the following sentence.

There is a _____ % chance that the offspring will have brown eyes.

## Differentiation of Cells

**4** Choose the correct words from the options given to complete the following sentence.

**structure**          **function**          **cells**

Differentiation is the result of _____ developing a specialised

_____ to carry out a specific _____ .

# Chromosomes, DNA and Genes

## Stem Cells

1 In which two places would you find stem cells?

a) ......................................................................................................................

b) ......................................................................................................................

## Chromosomes, DNA and Genes

2 What do the two strands of a DNA molecule coil together to form? Tick the correct option.

A   Double spring ⃝          B   Double twist ⃝

C   Double spiral ⃝          D   Double helix ⃝

HT

3 How do genes code for a particular characteristic?

.................................................................................................................................

.................................................................................................................................

## Genetic Disorders

4 What is an inherited disease? Tick the correct option.

A   A disease caused by microbes ⃝

B   A disease passed from person to person ⃝

C   A disease passed on from parent to child by genes ⃝

D   A self-inflicted disease ⃝

5 Fill in the missing words to complete the following sentences.

a) Huntington's disease is a disorder of the ..................................................................... .

It's caused by a ..................................... allele.

b) Cystic fibrosis is caused by a ..................................... allele. It must be inherited from both

parents. The parents might not have the disorder, but they might be ..................................... .

⃝

# Exchanging Materials

## Osmosis and Diffusion

**1** Fill in the missing words to complete the following sentences.

**a)** Water and dissolved substances automatically move _____ a concentration gradient.

**b)** They move from _____ concentrations to _____ concentrations.

## HT Active Transport

**2** What does active transport require? Tick the correct option.

    **A** It doesn't require anything ⬭    **B** It requires energy from respiration ⬭

    **C** It requires electrical energy ⬭    **D** It requires movement energy ⬭

**3** During active transport, how do substances move? Tick the correct option.

    **A** Against the concentration gradient ⬭    **B** Along the concentration gradient ⬭

    **C** In random directions ⬭    **D** Upwards ⬭

**4** Name two substances that can be moved by active transport.

**a)** _____

**b)** _____

## Exchanging Materials in Humans

**5** Fill in the missing words to complete the following sentence.

Humans have organ systems that are _____ to help the _____ of materials.

## Villi in the Small Intestine

**6** Which of the following statements about villi are true? Tick the **two** correct options.

    **A** They have a massive surface area ⬭

    **B** They have a small surface area ⬭

    **C** They have a small network of capillaries ⬭

    **D** They have an extensive network of capillaries ⬭

## The Breathing System

Revision Guide Reference: Page 57

**1** What part of the human skeleton protects the lungs? Tick the correct option.

**A** Diaphragm ◯ **B** Ribcage ◯

**C** Pelvis ◯ **D** Abdomen ◯

**2** What divides the thorax from the abdomen?

........................................................................................................................................

**3** Fill in the missing words to complete the following sentences.

Another name for the windpipe is the ........................................... . It has rings of ...........................................
to prevent it from collapsing.

**4** The windpipe divides into two tubes. What are these tubes called? Tick the correct option.

**A** Bronchioles ◯ **B** Ribs ◯

**C** Bronchi ◯ **D** Alveoli ◯

**5** Match the numbers on the diagram with the words listed below. Write the appropriate numbers in the boxes provided.

**A** Ribs ◯

**B** Bronchus ◯

**C** Diaphragm ◯

**D** Windpipe ◯

# Exchanging Materials

## Alveoli in the Lungs

**1** What is an alveolus? Tick the correct option.

    **A** A blood vessel ⬭

    **B** An air tube ⬭

    **C** An air sac ⬭

    **D** A bone ⬭

**2** Which substances are exchanged at the alveoli? Tick the correct option.

    **A** Oxygen and water ⬭

    **B** Oxygen and nitrogen ⬭

    **C** Oxygen and carbon dioxide ⬭

    **D** Carbon dioxide and water ⬭

**3 a)** Which substance diffuses from the blood into the alveoli?

    _____

    **b)** Which substance diffuses from the alveoli into the blood?

    _____

**4** Circle the correct options in the following sentences.

There are **no / hundreds of / thousands of / millions of** alveoli in the lungs. They are **close to / far away from / in / part of** the blood capillaries.

**5** Which of the following are features of the alveoli? Tick the **two** correct options.

    **A** Good blood supply ⬭

    **B** Large surface area ⬭

    **C** No walls ⬭

    **D** Poor blood supply ⬭

    **E** Thick walls ⬭

    **F** Small surface area ⬭

## Exchanging Materials in Plants

**1** Fill in the missing words to complete the following sentences.

a) Leaves have a _____ surface area in order to make them very efficient at photosynthesis.

b) A plant's leaves are usually _____, thin and _____.

**2** What is water loss from a plant known as? Tick the correct option.

A  Transpiration ⃝                    B  Evaporation ⃝

C  Circulation ⃝                      D  Dehydration ⃝

**3** List the three conditions that would increase the rate of transpiration.

a) _____

b) _____

c) _____

**4** What controls the size of the stomata? Tick the correct option.

A  Soldier cells ⃝                    B  Guard cells ⃝

C  Keeper cells ⃝                     D  Defence cells ⃝

**5** a) In what conditions are the stomata open?

_____

b) What happens when the stomata are open?

_____

**6** a) In what conditions are the stomata closed?

_____

b) Why do the stomata close?

_____

c) What else has to stop as a result of the stomata closing?

_____

# The Circulation System

**The Circulation System**

**1** Fill in the missing words to complete the following sentences.

a) The circulation system consists of your _____, your _____

_____ and your _____.

b) The blood carries _____ and _____ to all body cells. The

blood carries _____ away from all body cells.

**2 a)** What do we call blood that contains oxygen?

_____

b) What do we call blood that contains carbon dioxide?

_____

**3** Circle the correct options in the following sentences.

a) Blood is pumped to the **lungs / stomach / heart / brain** so carbon dioxide can be exchanged for
**water / nitrogen / oxygen / mineral ions**.

b) Blood passes through the heart **once / twice / three times / four times** on each circuit.

**4 a)** Which blood vessel carries blood away from the heart? Tick the correct option.

A  An artery ◯

B  A vein ◯

C  A valve ◯

D  A capillary ◯

b) Which blood vessel carries blood towards the heart? Tick the correct option.

A  An artery ◯

B  A vein ◯

C  A valve ◯

D  A capillary ◯

## The Circulation System

Revision Guide Reference: Page 59

**1** Match the numbers on the diagram with the words listed below. Write the appropriate numbers in the boxes provided.

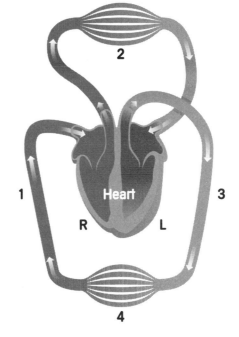

**A** Artery ◯

**B** Vein ◯

**C** Capillaries in the body ◯

**D** Capillaries in the lungs ◯

## The Blood

**2** Blood is made up of four components. What are they?

**a)** ...................................................................................................................

**b)** ...................................................................................................................

**c)** ...................................................................................................................

**d)** ...................................................................................................................

**3** Fill in the missing words to complete the following sentences.

Plasma transports carbon dioxide from the ........................................ to the ........................................,

and it transports ........................................ from the small intestine to the organs. It also transports other

waste products from the ........................................ to the ........................................ .

**4** Fill in the missing words to complete the following sentences.

Red blood cells transport ........................................ from the lungs to the organs. They contain lots of

........................................, which combines with oxygen to form ........................................ .

# Respiration

## Aerobic Respiration

**1** What is aerobic respiration? Tick the correct option.

    **A** Respiration in the absence of oxygen ⬭

    **B** Respiration in the presence of oxygen ⬭

    **C** Respiration that produces lactic acid ⬭

    **D** Respiration that uses carbon dioxide ⬭

**2** When does aerobic respiration occur?

_____

**3** What is the correct equation for aerobic respiration? Tick the correct option.

    **A** Glucose + Carbon dioxide ⟶ Water + Oxygen ⬭

    **B** Glucose + Carbon dioxide ⟶ Energy + Oxygen ⬭

    **C** Glucose + Oxygen ⟶ Water + Carbon dioxide + Energy ⬭

    **D** Water + Oxygen ⟶ Glucose + Carbon dioxide + Energy ⬭

**4** Fill in the missing words to complete the following sentences.

    **a)** Energy from respiration is used to enable muscles to _____ .

    **b)** Aerobic respiration is a very _____ way of producing energy.

**5** How do glucose and oxygen get to the respiring cells? Tick the correct option.

    **A** By the bloodstream ⬭

    **B** By eating ⬭

    **C** By drinking ⬭

    **D** By osmosis ⬭

**6** Fill in the missing words to complete the following sentence.

One molecule of _____ produced by aerobic respiration provides

_____ times as much energy as anaerobic respiration.

## Aerobic Respiration

**1** List three ways in which the water produced in aerobic respiration is lost from the body.

a) ................................................................................................................

b) ................................................................................................................

c) ................................................................................................................

**2** List three things that the energy produced in aerobic respiration is used for.

a) ................................................................................................................

b) ................................................................................................................

c) ................................................................................................................

## Anaerobic Respiration

**3** What is anaerobic respiration? Tick the correct option.

**A** Respiration in the absence of oxygen ◯ **B** Respiration in the presence of oxygen ◯

**C** Respiration that produces lactic acid ◯ **D** Respiration that uses carbon dioxide ◯

**4** Circle the correct option in the following sentence.

If your muscles are subjected to long periods of **light / vigorous / slow** activity, they become fatigued.

HT

**5** What is the waste product of anaerobic respiration? Tick the correct option.

**A** Hydrochloric acid ◯ **B** Sulfuric acid ◯

**C** Lactic acid ◯ **D** Aerobic respiration ◯

**6** Fill in the missing words to complete the following sentences.

a) Anaerobic respiration occurs when the lungs and bloodstream cannot deliver enough

.......................................... to the cells.

b) When lactic acid builds up in the tissues, the muscles become ............................... .

c) The amount of oxygen needed to break down the lactic acid in tissues is called the

.......................................... .

# Respiration

## HT Anaerobic Respiration

**1** What is the word equation for anaerobic respiration? Tick the correct option.

    **A**   Glucose + Oxygen ➡ Energy + Lactic acid   ⬭

    **B**   Glucose + Oxygen ➡ Energy   ⬭

    **C**   Glucose ➡ Energy   ⬭

    **D**   Glucose ➡ Energy + Lactic acid   ⬭

**2** Is more energy produced during aerobic respiration or anaerobic respiration?

_____

**3** Are the following sentences **true** or **false**?

    **a)** Lactic acid makes the muscles feel tired and rubbery. _____

    **b)** Anaerobic respiration produces a small amount of energy quickly. _____

    **c)** Anaerobic respiration is more efficient than aerobic respiration. _____

## Exercise and the Body

**4** During exercise, changes take place in the body. Which of the following are true? Tick the **three** correct options.

    **A**   Your heart rate decreases   ⬭

    **B**   Your heart rate increases   ⬭

    **C**   Blood flow to your muscles increases   ⬭

    **D**   Blood flow to your muscles decreases   ⬭

    **E**   Breathing rate increases   ⬭

    **F**   Breathing rate decreases   ⬭

**5** Fill in the missing words to complete the following sentences.

    **a)** During exercise, the supply of oxygen and _____ is _____ .

    This speeds up the removal of _____ .

    **b)** Animal starch, also known as _____ is broken down into

    _____ .

## The Kidneys

**1** How many kidneys do most people have? Tick the correct option.

**A** One ◯    **B** Two ◯

**C** Three ◯    **D** Four ◯

**2** Give **three** functions of the kidneys.

a) ..............................................................................................................................................................

b) ..............................................................................................................................................................

c) ..............................................................................................................................................................

**3** When a person's kidneys fail, why does this result in death if left untreated?

..............................................................................................................................................................

..............................................................................................................................................................

**4** What two important tissues is each kidney made up of?

a) ..............................................................................................................................................................

b) ..............................................................................................................................................................

## How the Kidneys Function

**5** Fill in the missing words to complete the following sentence.

Unwanted substances end up in millions of tiny .................................................., which eventually join together

to form the ...................................................... .

**6** Where is urine stored before it leaves the body? Tick the correct option.

**A** Large intestine ◯    **B** Rectum ◯

**C** Kidney ◯    **D** Bladder ◯

**7** What is meant by the term 'selective reabsorption'? Tick the correct option.

**A** Excess substances are released ◯

**B** Water and small molecules are squeezed out of the blood ◯

**C** Useful substances return to the blood ◯

**D** The kidneys stop working ◯

◯

# The Kidneys and Dialysis

## Dialysis Machines

**1** Fill in the missing words to complete the following sentences.

a) In a dialysis machine the blood flows between a ............................................................................................
membrane.

b) Dialysis fluid contains the same concentrations of useful substances as ............................................................, so

............................................................ and essential ............................................................ ions aren't lost through diffusion.

**2** Why does dialysis have to be repeated on a regular basis?

................................................................................................................................................................................................

## Kidney Transplants

**3** What is the term used for a person who gives one of their healthy kidneys to a person with kidney failure? Tick the correct option.

A Donor ⬭

B Surrogate ⬭

C Dependent ⬭

D Samaritan ⬭

**4** Is the following statement **true** or **false**?

Kidney transplants are necessary when only one kidney works. ............................................................

**5** a) What is the main problem with kidney transplants?

................................................................................................................................................................................................

b) What causes this problem?

................................................................................................................................................................................................

c) Give three precautions that could be taken to prevent problems with kidney transplants.

i) ..........................................................................................................................................................................

ii) ..........................................................................................................................................................................

iii) ..........................................................................................................................................................................

# Using Microorganisms

## Bacteria

Revision Guide Reference: Page 64

**1** Which foods or drinks are made with the help of bacteria? Tick the **two** correct options.

A Cheese ◯   B Wine ◯

C Yoghurt ◯   D Bread ◯

**2** Are the following statements **true** or **false**?

a) Bacteria vary in shape. ........................

b) Bacteria don't have a cell wall. ........................

c) Bacteria have a distinct nucleus. ........................

## Yeast

**3** Which foods or drinks are made with the help of yeast? Tick the **two** correct options.

A Beer ◯   B Yoghurt ◯

C Bread ◯   D Cheese ◯

**4** Are the following statements **true** or **false**?

a) Yeast is a single-celled organism with a nucleus. ........................

b) Each yeast cell has cytoplasm. ........................

## How Yeast Works

**5** What is the anaerobic respiration of yeast called?

........................

**6** Circle the correct options in the following sentences.

a) Yeast can respire without oxygen (**anaerobic / aerobic** respiration) to produce ethanol / water and carbon dioxide.

b) Yeast can respire with oxygen (**anaerobic / aerobic** respiration) to produce ethanol / water and carbon dioxide.

**7** Why is aerobic respiration better for yeast?

........................

........................

# Using Microorganisms

## Using Yeast in Baking

**1** When using yeast in baking, what makes the dough rise? Tick the correct option.

**A** Oxygen ☐      **B** Carbon dioxide ☐

**C** Hydrogen ☐      **D** Water ☐

**2** What happens to any alcohol produced whilst bread is baking?

_____

## Using Yeast in Brewing

**3** What process is used to make beer? Tick the correct option.

**A** Malting ☐      **B** Waxing ☐

**C** Baking ☐      **D** Distilling ☐

**4** Fill in the missing words to complete the following sentences.

The starch in barley is broken down into a sugary solution by _____. Yeast is then

added to the solution and _____ takes place.

## Using Bacteria to Make Yoghurt

**5** Fill in the missing word to complete the following sentence.

Lactic acid causes milk to _____.

**6** Draw lines between the boxes to match each product to its sugar supply.

| Products | Sugar Supply |
|----------|--------------|
| Bread | Lactose |
| Wine | Grapes |
| Yoghurt | Starch in barley |
| Beer | Sugar added to flour |

## Growing Microorganisms

**1** What is mycoprotein made from? Tick the correct option.

   **A**  A bacterium  ◯

   **B**  A fungus  ◯

   **C**  A virus  ◯

   **D**  A protozoan  ◯

**2** Penicillin is produced in fermenters from a strain of penicillium. What is penicillium?

_____

**3** Match the labels **1–3** with the words below. Write the appropriate number in the boxes provided.

   **A**  Air supply  ◯

   **B**  Temperature probe  ◯

   **C**  Outlet tap  ◯

pH probe

Stirrer

**3**

**4** Why does a fermenter contain a stirrer?

**1**  **2**

_____

_____

## Fuel Production

**5** Fill in the missing words to complete the following sentences.

   **a)**  Biogas mainly consists of _____ .

   **b)**  Biogas can be produced by animal or plant _____ that contains a lot of

   _____ .

**6** For ethanol to be produced from the sugar in sugar cane, which process needs to be used? Tick the correct option.

   **A**  Aerobic fermentation  ◯

   **B**  Anaerobic fermentation  ◯

   **C**  Aerobic distillation  ◯

# Growing Microorganisms

## Preparing a Culture Medium

**1** When microorganisms are cultured in the laboratory, what are they grown on? Tick the correct option.

**A** Agar ◯　　　　　**B** Plasma ◯

**C** Water ◯　　　　　**D** Soil ◯

**2** In order to culture a particular microorganism, what types of nutrients might be needed in the culture medium? Tick the **four** correct options.

**A** Pesticides ◯　　　　**B** Proteins ◯

**C** Fertilisers ◯　　　　**D** Carbohydrates ◯

**E** Vitamins ◯　　　　**F** Mineral ions ◯

**3** Give two properties of agar.

**a)** ......................................................................................................................

**b)** ......................................................................................................................

## Preparing Uncontaminated Cultures

**4 a)** Why must you take care not to contaminate agar plates with unwanted microorganisms?

..............................................................................................................................

..............................................................................................................................

**b)** What is an autoclave?

..............................................................................................................................

..............................................................................................................................

**c)** How would you sterilise an inoculating loop?

..............................................................................................................................

..............................................................................................................................

**d)** Why should the Petri dish, containing the agar, be sealed with tape?

..............................................................................................................................

# Notes